How We All Went
RAW

by

THE TOP RAW MEN™

Charles Nungesser

and

Stephen Malachi

Published by
In the Beginning Health Ministry
2443 S. Paseo Loma Circle
Mesa, Arizona 85202

Copyright© 2003
ISBN: 0-9740378-5-0

First Printing October 2002
Second Printing January 2003
Third Printing July 2003

TOP RAW MEN-U
now serving ...

TOP RAW MEN-U
(continued)

Foreword

The Top Raw Men™ have a unique story to tell and valuable insights to share, displaying wisdom beyond their years. They have persevered to overcome opposition and setbacks of living in a cooked food world. Their search urged them to push forward with sheer determination in pursuit of something better than they had experienced so far. As a result, they have reaped better health and a better life. They are leaders for our generation, who sincerely desire to help people get well and live healthy lives.

It is interesting that they rarely had spent much time cooking their food before, mainly choosing to make simpler packaged and prepared foods. Once they started eating raw food exclusively, their "hidden chef talent" seemed to come alive!

You have enjoyed many of these recipes as cooked foods for years. Now you can experience the unique creativity of eating them raw. Go ahead—indulge as you explore this book with a spirit of adventure and savor the flavor in these pages! You are in for a real treat!

Mary Lynn Russo
Editor

Preface

The search for good health and stamina led Charles and Stephen to make a commitment to eat only raw food for one year. What started out as an easy experiment soon became very difficult because, "you can only eat so many salads and smoothies." Their stomachs' search for something else to eat resulted in many attempts to develop more satisfying raw food combinations. To their taste buds' delight, they created many new and delicious recipes.

They started raw food potlucks for young people to share favorite dishes and exchange recipes. The gatherings then grew to include people of all ages. Encouragement and creative ideas came from associating with other people who eat raw food and are seeking a healthy lifestyle.

They learned that eating raw is the way the body can restore and maintain health. Confirmation of this comes from their personal experience and the testimony of others. The Top Raw Men™, Charles and Stephen, are committed to eating this way!

And now, after close to three years on their raw food diet, this unconventional "cookbook" is born.

Acknowledgements

With hearts full of gratitude, we want to thank all who have attended our raw food potlucks. You have encouraged us in our quest for good health, and we hope we have encouraged you as well. We all need accountability when the spirit is willing, but the flesh is weak.

This book has been made possible with the help of many kind, generous people. Mrs. Coleen Takemoto has provided insight and a trusty camera to help this book come together in a timely manner. Her desire to help young people help others shines brightly throughout this project. We also thank her husband, Arnold, for his input, assistance, and sharing his wife's precious time away from their business. Hats off to Dr. Sam and Sue Walters for their support and creative ideas like Top Hats for the Top Raw Men™ . Alex Johnston is the computer graphic genius that created the great cover layout and design. One picture says a thousand words.

We are grateful to Mary Lynn Russo for her dedication in overseeing this project. Her unending efforts to keep the book moving on a tight production schedule was invaluable. We also thank Suzanne Elliott for proof reading and Janet Cook for the addition of the Top Hat Tips. We are indebted to Elise Darbro for guidance in editor's etiquette.

We are also grateful to Linda Penn and Sandra Barnes who took time away from their busy work schedules to help in marketing and promotion. Ann Ault Owen enthusiastically showed ways to expand beyond our community. Lillian Murdock has been our prayer warrior. She also encouraged us to be chefs years before we realized it. Thanks to Carmen Zesati-Rodriguez (Stephen's mother) who was the source of many of Stephen's raw recipe ideas. "I love you Mama." We could never repay George & Peggy Nungesser for the countless hours of help and for all the necessary mundane details. To all our friends, thank you for your great ideas, encouragement, prayers, love and support that made this book become a reality.

God is great, God is good, let us thank Him for RAW food!

WHO RAW! *About the Authors*
Charles Nungesser

Charles has dealt with health challenges since he was very young. A severe food reaction at the age of one sent him to the Emergency Room in Anaphylactic Shock. His entire body had swelled to twice its normal size. Later his Allergist diagnosed him to be allergic to all foods except chocolate and onions. He would tease his family and say, "I can have all the chocolate covered onions I want." Yeah, right. Yuck! When and where would his next allergic food reaction take place? Instead of meal time being a time of refreshment, it became a very difficult and tormenting time. Would his lips tingle and his throat itch with his next bite of food? Would his next meal start the path to the ER?

When he was 20 years old his throat became swollen around a piece of broccoli, and he could not breathe. A co-worker quickly used the Heimlich maneuver and saved his life. Charles was also an asthmatic. He could not leave the house without his inhaler. Physical activity, such as snowboarding in the cold, high altitude, was very difficult prior to a raw food diet. Now it's a regular winter sport!

Since changing his diet, his food allergies and asthma are also gone. Today Charles enjoys a variety of physical activities and is on the Dean's List at Arizona State University majoring in Fine Arts.

4

Stephen Malachi

As Stephen became a teenager, he struggled with several health challenges. He had severe acne, migraine headaches, and was 40 pounds overweight. Any one of these challenges alone can be overwhelming for a teenager, but three at the same time was devastating. He started his raw food adventure seeking a clearer complexion. Not only did Stephen's acne go away on a raw food diet, but to his amazement, his migraine headaches disappeared and he lost 40 pounds as well! He has great skin and health, and his personal gifts shine forth through his outgoing personality.

Currently, Stephen is an honor roll student at Mesa Community College. Can a raw food diet affect your mental capabilities for better grades too? Stephen believes so, and he is majoring in Biochemistry. He appreciates the added energy he has for studying.

One of Stephen's favorite pastimes is juicing. He loves to experiment with juicing several fruits or several vegetables together. Different juice combinations seem to energize different parts of the body. Carrot juice or carrots and apples juiced together are tasty drinks. But Stephen likes to juice the green plants. Juicing kale, endive, and arugula together can taste pretty bitter. If it doesn't taste sweet, then bottoms up anyway because Stephen likes to say, "The more bitter, the more better!"

<u>NOTES</u>

WHY RAW?

One of the first questions that we usually hear when we say to people "we only eat raw food" is, "why?" This is a legitimate question. We felt it was important to set forth a logical, science-based explanation as a precursor to our recipes. Before we begin, however, we would like to state what we absolutely know from experience to be true about the raw food diet.

We have seen tremendous positive changes in our health, as well as witnessed many health benefits in others who eat a predominantly raw food diet. We have seen major turnarounds in cancer, heart disease, diabetes, hypoglycemia, thyroid disorders, hormone imbalance, weight problems and many other health struggles. After seeing all these benefits, we were convinced there is *something powerful* to raw foods. This led us to research the reason behind it all. After having reviewed the latest scientific literature, we present here a valid and testable hypothesis as to why people experience such a difference in their health on a raw food diet.

RAW FOODS 101

As we elaborate on the various points that relate to eating food in its raw and unheated state, we would like you to hold a specific image in your mind. This image is central to understanding how to be healthy by eating raw. The picture that we would like you to envision is *the human body, with all its functions, as a living chemical factory*. We cannot emphasize the importance of this awareness. A major alteration in any chemical system is the beginning of all dysfunction or sickness. Metabolism is the broad word used to refer to all the chemical reactions that take place within the body. The proper maintenance and balance of all these chemical reactions is termed homeostasis. To re-emphasize, a disruption in any metabolic pathway that brings the body out of homeostasis for a prolonged period of time is disease.

Although this may seem obvious or even a little redundant, most people do not make a connection between what they eat and its impact on their body chemistry. We continually consume foods that are known to have carcinogens and other toxins in them. At the same time we neglect the foods that maintain proper body chemistry, such as raw fruits and vegetables. The reason this habit continues is because there are no immediate consequences.

What we fail to realize is that, as long as we make unhealthy food choices, small changes in our body chemistry are occurring day after day, month after month, year after year. By middle age, or sooner, all sorts of chronic degenerative diseases mysteriously start appearing.

Please do not misunderstand us, we are aware that a small percentage of the population have genetic malfunctions, which can alter their body chemistry regardless of their diet. However, in our opinion, the majority of diseases that we are seeing, especially in the United States, are directly correlated to our diet. There are many things that can negatively alter our body chemistry, but we are only going to focus on free radicals and enzymes (or the lack thereof).

FREE RADICALS AND ANTIOXIDANTS

What is a free radical? Why are they harmful? Where do they come from? A free radical on a chemical level is basically a molecule with an unpaired electron. Unpaired electrons, in molecules, don't like to be alone. They will react with a nearby molecule by stealing its electron. This is known as oxidation. The nearby molecule that lost its electron then becomes a free radical and steals an electron from some other close by molecule. This progression leads to many oxidative reaction events that produce hazardous byproduct chemicals along the way.

Rather than trying to grasp everything that occurs on the chemical level, just remember that any abnormality in the body chemistry for prolonged periods of time, such as free radical damage, will cause disease.

Antioxidants have the ability to halt electrons without becoming free radicals themselves. Vitamin C and vitamin E are examples of the many nutrients that operate as antioxidants. At this point, we would like to make it clear that we are not advocating the use of antioxidant supplements. There are plenty of antioxidants in raw foods.

Free radicals have been shown to cause widespread damage. They disrupt the transport of nutrients into and out of the cells. Free radicals also alter the function of cell proteins and DNA, which can lead to inherited defects.

10

A common term used to describe the damaging process of free radicals is oxidative stress. Oxidative stress causes disease by destroying the valuable components of cells. It also signals inappropriate activities within metabolism, which can take the body even further out of the balanced state of homeostasis.

Everyone has seen oxidative stress and probably without actually realizing it. For example, after a car has spent many days in the blazing hot sun, it has undergone severe free radical damage. The faded paint, the brittle deterioration of the tires, the cracks and hardness in the dashboard are all examples of free radical damage. We gave you these illustrations so you can conceptually internalize the havoc that takes place when your body is flooded with free radicals. Scientists have shown how oxidative stress has a role in early aging, cancer, arthritis, cataracts, and heart disease.

We all encounter environmental free radicals everyday. Such things as air pollution are impossible to avoid. However dietary free radicals are a different story; we can make choices to help avoid them. The easiest way is to eat food in its raw, live state (not heated over 105°F). There are two reasons for this.

First, cooking food increases the amount of free radicals in them (which we explain in the following paragraph). Second, fruits and vegetables in their raw, unheated state have an abundance of antioxidants.

All foods will eventually deteriorate and form free radicals within themselves. Just as a car is more damaged the longer it sits in the hot sun, the same is basically true with all food. This is the main reason why it is ideal to eat our food when it is freshly harvested, or soon after. In that raw state, it has the most nutritive value.

Heat is a type of energy that speeds up the rate at which normal chemical reactions occur. It facilitates unneeded chemical reactions that would never have occurred. An egg white left sitting in a bowl will eventually oxidize. However, it would never naturally change into the solid white, rubbery substance that it is converted into when it is fried or boiled. Understand this fact: when you cook your food, you are putting it through a chemical reaction. The higher the temperature and the longer it cooks, the more it is oxidized—thereby increasing the free radical concentration. (An example of a carcinogenic reaction is the black crust on a piece of grilled fish.)

As we explained earlier, free radicals have detrimental effects on our health. Heart disease is the number one killer in the United States. We would like to explain how free radicals contribute to this epidemic.

When your diet contains a high quantity of oxidized food (cooked food), you have a high concentration of free radicals circulating in your blood stream. These free radicals can accumulate within the arterial walls, which can cause the oxidation of LDL (bad) cholesterol. This oxidation causes a change in the LDL's structure and function. The oxidized LDL then accelerates the formation of artery-clogging plaques. In contrast, consuming an abundance of raw fruits and vegetables will strengthen your antioxidant defenses against LDL oxidation.

When our body has been given adequate nutrition, it has an enzyme defense system that can disarm the most harmful oxidants. This enzyme system is dependent on selenium, copper, manganese, and zinc. Without an adequate amount of these minerals, this line of defense weakens. Even when our enzyme system is fully functional, we possess little defense against the lesser harmful oxidants. Just because they are "less" harmful does not mean they cannot alter our body chemistry.

These less harmful oxidants, in large quantities, are precisely the ones that have been shown to contribute to cancer, heart disease, early aging, etc. The safest way to protect yourself from free radicals is to significantly decrease your intake of them from dietary sources. In other words, decrease eating cooked food while at the same time increasing your consumption of antioxidants from raw fruits and vegetables.

ENZYMES

As we stated earlier, we have been asked many times by various people why we only eat raw foods. We used to enthusiastically reply with one simple word, *"enzymes!"* However, we have learned that the vastness of this component requires at least a 15-minute explanation.

Generally, people that we bumped into weren't interested in giving up cooked food unless they had some major health problems and wanted the raw food diet benefits. We learned that it was more efficient to answer with, "We eat this way for health reasons. If you are interested and have a few minutes we can explain the details." This response has worked well for us.

Enzymes are the primary reason for eating a raw food diet. There are many other reasons for not cooking your food such as the formation of free radicals, the loss of water, the breakdown of proteins, the increase of white blood cell immune response, the conversion of mineral chelates to oxides and carbonates (which makes minerals non-absorbable), etc. However as important as these principles are, they are still secondary to the principle of enzymes.

Enzymes are catalysts, which speed up chemical reactions or, in other words, they are the body's work force. Our body requires enzymes for healing, thinking, breathing, digestion, etc. All food in its raw, unheated state has the necessary enzymes within itself to break itself down. For example, the chemical processes that change a banana from green to yellow and eventually brown are all enzyme reactions. The banana is basically "digesting" itself. When you eat a ripe banana, while in the upper region of the stomach, it digests itself within your body.

Enzymes, like all other proteins, are very sensitive to heat. When an enzyme is exposed to excessive heat it is denatured or loses its function. Most enzymes denature at approximately 115-130°F. If you heat a banana above 130°F while it is still green, it will never ripen and turn yellow for the enzymes have been completely destroyed. The same thing happens when raw foods are cooked. When you eat something that no longer has its enzymes intact, your body is forced to compensate by expending energy for digestion. This unnecessary stress can lead to disease and premature aging.

The pancreas is the main organ in the body that produces digestive enzymes. When we eat foods that have no enzymes in them, our pancreas will be forced to pick up the extra slack, with detrimental effects. Dr. Edward Howell in his excellent book, *Enzyme Nutrition*,[1] shows the ill effects of an enzyme deficient diet. He performed a controlled experiment with two groups of laboratory mice. One group of mice had cooked food and the other had the same food raw.

After several weeks he dissected them and observed that the pancreases of the mice that had been fed cooked food had swollen to nearly three times the size of the mice that were fed raw food. Such a massive amount of stress had been placed on the pancreas, in order to compensate for the lack of enzymes, that it caused major swelling. There were also other ill effects on the rest of the organs—some shrunk and others such as the thyroid swelled. We highly recommend Dr. Howell's book.

How do these results translate into the human body experience? Well, we can (for explanatory purposes only) separate enzymes into two categories—digestive and metabolic. Digestive enzymes, for the most part, are more complex and require more energy to build than your average metabolic enzyme.

When we eat food that has lost its enzymes, our pancreas compensates for the deficiency in order to facilitate digestion by using molecules that would have normally gone to making metabolic enzymes. The rest of the metabolic functions in the body suffer because of the expended energy lost to digestion of cooked food during enzyme production.

We only have a certain amount of the basic building block molecules and only a certain amount of energy with which to build them. Healing, thinking, blood clotting, resting, physical activity, and any other metabolic pathway that you can think of all suffer loss. Therefore they do not function as well as they should because of the extra load placed on the pancreas when eating enzyme deficient food.

The reverse of this is the cause of the "hunger factor" when a person first transitions to a raw diet. The pancreas is in the habit of producing massive amounts of enzymes to digest cooked food. Consequently when food contains all its necessary enzymes, it is broken down twice as fast and your stomach is ready for the next round sooner. After time the body adjusts and our pancreas goes back to its regular size. (For those with an eye of scrutiny, we are aware that the pancreas produces a small amount of enzymes even when 100% of our food contains its necessary enzymes—only a fraction relative to an enzyme-deficient diet though.)

There is also a misconception that we hear quite often, mainly from pre-med students, when we explain the function of enzymes. As we explained, enzymes are heat sensitive. However, they are also pH sensitive and some are even sensitive to light. (pH is the acid/alkaline balance indicator of body fluids.)

The misconception is that it does not matter if our food has enzymes in it or not because the strong acidity of our stomach denatures the enzymes. The major difference between a heat denatured enzyme and a pH-denatured enzyme is that once an enzyme has been denatured by excessive heat, it will never return to a functional state. This is not true for many of the pH-denatured enzymes. Once the enzyme is returned to its proper pH, it regains its function. Dr. Gabriel Cousens also deals with this misconception in more detail, so we felt that it would be beneficial to include a quote from him:

> "People have been successfully ingesting pineapple enzyme, bromelain, for years, as a treatment for muscle and joint inflammation. Research with radioactive tracers shows that at least 40% of the pineapple enzyme is absorbed into our system in an intact form. This is simple, but straightforward evidence. Live cell analysis experimentation has shown that within ten minutes after ingesting enzymes, red blood cells become un-clumped. Something is happening in the blood after the enzymes are ingested that suggests the enzymes are effective in the blood. The most important scientific evidence ... about enzymes comes from a research paper by Dr. Michael Gardner at the School of Biomedical Sciences in England, titled 'Gastrointestinal Absorption of Intact Proteins' published in the *Annual Review of Nutrition* in 1988. After his extensive review of the literature, Dr. Gardner concludes: 'the concordance between results obtained by

independent workers using different experimental approaches is now so strong that we cannot fail to accept that intact proteins and high-molecular-fragments therefore do cross the gastrointestinal tract in humans and animals (both newborns and adults). In other words, the live enzymes ... are able to cross the gastrointestinal tract in their intact form and, therefore, can have the healing affect on the body as claimed by live food advocates."[2]

One last heads-up as you make the transition to a raw food diet. You will inevitably encounter the curious and the cynical. Both will stretch you. The information we have provided is a good start. However, your health is your own responsibility, so learn as much as you can about how to be healthy. Do not let conflicting ideas about health discourage your search. We encourage you to even test and verify the things that we have presented to you. *"Prove all things; hold fast that which is good. Abstain from all appearance of evil."*[3]

Most of all, enjoy our recipes!

NOTES

HOW RAW?

There are as many ways to eat raw food as there are fruits and vegetables. The following are some raw food diets: mono-food diet (one type of food per meal), fruitarian (only fruit), and ordinary raw (like us). We feel best when we consume an array of fruits, vegetables, sprouts, fresh juices, nuts, seeds, and cold pressed oils. VARIETY IS KEY FOR A WELL BALANCED RAW FOOD DIET!

Getting Started

If you make the transition to 100% raw foods, you may experience the "hunger factor." We describe this as the inability to keep your stomach feeling full. You may be sensitive to this for about a month. Your stomach is the first part of your body that will begin to adjust, so be patient. During this period we consumed massive amounts of smoothies and salads. As soon as we were done drinking one smoothie, we were in the process of making another. During this period, eat as much raw food as you need. We recommend green juices for their concentrated minerals, smoothies for their taste and cleansing power, and hearty salads with lots of raw fats, such as avocados, to fill you up. (You may need to avoid fats if you have serious health challenges). This was the time when we came up with some of our best smoothie recipes. We experienced the truth of "necessity is the mother of all inventions." Some good entrées from this book to implement into your diet at this time will be the Tacos, Everybody's Favorite Salad, Hummus, all the smoothies—especially The Fat Lover, all the juices—especially the ones with dark greens. These entrées are high in fat, which will satisfy much of your hunger.

Key Kitchen Appliances

<u>Blender</u> The blender is probably the most frequently used machine in our kitchen. We use it to make soups, smoothies, "cheese" sauces, dressings, nut milks, "ice cream," etc. If there was only one kitchen appliance we could have, it would be a blender. Of course like everything else, there are many different types of blenders and prices. Our favorite is the Vita-Mix®. The price is $400 plus, and it's well worth it! This machine has no problem blending nuts and seeds into nut butter. Less expensive machines are great for smoothies, soups, dressings and nut milks, but you will have to be careful not to burn out the motor when making nut cheeses.

<u>Food Processor</u> Food processors are a great timesaver in the kitchen. They come with three different cutting blades, which are all invaluable.

Grating Blade
We use it to grate hard fruits and vegetables, i.e, our Spanish Rice.

Slicing Blade
Great when making food for a large dinner party, i.e., cutting lettuce, cabbage, etc.

S Blade
Resembles the use of the blender, great for our Universal Pie Crust, Salsa and also making pâtés, i.e., our Taco Meat. We've even made smoothies this way.

There are many different kinds of food processors, and they all seem to work fine except in one area—blending nuts, seeds, and dates. We recommend the Cuisinart® because of its powerful motor—there are less expensive ones that work well too.

Juicer Juicers range from $50 to $2000. Just make sure whichever one you buy, you use it. The more you spend, the better the quality of juice. We recommend the Samson® or Green Star® 3000. These two can juice wheat grass.

Dehydrator A great tool to make "mock" (imitation) foods. Ours runs nonstop. We are from the southwest, which means one thing—Mexican food, chips and salsa. When we first went raw, this was our greatest craving. We tried our hardest to make a chip substitute for over a year. We now have a chip substitute, thanks to the dehydrator.

Sometimes it's hard to find a place that sells these items. You can try a local kitchen supply store. Or you can order them from <u>In the Beginning Health Ministry</u> (888) 661-7401.

If you can't afford these appliances, don't get discouraged. All you really need is a cutting board, the larger the better, and a sharp knife. Watch out for your fingers! Another good addition to a raw food kitchen are large mixing bowls—glass or stainless steel works best, but you can find large plastic bowls at dollar stores.

All of these appliances make for one awesome raw food kitchen! To remain raw consistently, all you really need is a friend or more to encourage you with your commitment and perhaps go raw with you.

Raw Food Friends

We are spoiled because we hold each other accountable as the Top Raw Men™. We have many other friends, mostly out of state, who struggle trying to do it by themselves. We recommend you find a raw food potluck to attend in your own city. If there isn't one, start your own raw food potluck; we have helpful hints on how to do that.

Traveling

When we're on the road we find our "fast food" at grocery stores. Nothing is easier or quicker than some bananas or half of a watermelon. When eating at restaurants ask the waiter to make you a special salad, which consists of all their raw vegetables served with lemon wedges and extra virgin cold pressed olive oil. It's usually a hit or miss. So use our "Letter to the Chef" as a guide (located in back of book). Make a copy of it and carry it with you when you go out to eat. Planning ahead never hurts; try packing dried fruit and nuts. Where there's a will to eat raw food, there's a way to eat raw food. Charles' brother George Nungesser, one of the original Top Raw Men™, is a commercial airline pilot. He's gone from home half the week, and he still finds a way to eat all raw.

Don't get discouraged! Remember it's not what you just ate, it's what your'e planning to eat raw.

Where to Shop

The absolute best place to get raw food is straight from your own garden. We like to get our raw food from local farmer's markets. Organic is far superior to conventional, so do your best when shopping. Organic produce has much more vitamin and mineral content intact than inorganic, chemically laden, genetically altered food. Other good places to buy raw food are co-ops or health food stores. For exotic items like durians or young coconuts, try Chinese markets. When trying to find specialty items such as Nama Shoyu (raw soy sauce) or coco butter, try ordering it online www.rawfood.com.

WARNING!!! If you're a single man or woman and you plan not to be single, then heed these words: Don't, we repeat don't, think you're going to meet a raw foodist for a mate. Learn from our mistakes...we've found women and we've found raw foodists—we've yet to find our Top Raw Women! Just be an example of taking care of your health and others will perhaps follow.

Forgive us for writing that, but it had to be said. We ourselves were tricked into becoming raw foodists. Someone told us there were a lot of honeys who were raw. Later we found out they were talking about honeydew melons.

Preparation
When looking through our recipes you will notice that some of them take an extended amount of time to prepare. We suggest you pick up a goal setting book. Dr. Jeff

Myers has a few we recommend. All that is really needed is a little planning ahead. So put a smile on your face, hold your head high and tell yourself repeatedly, "I can do this!" Since some of the recipes take a while to make, we tell people to double or triple the recipe—especially when making chips—they store well and they're always nice to have around.

NOTES

28

WHAT RAW?

NOTES

30

DELICIOUS
SALADS

CHARLES' COLE SLAW

time: 20 minutes

In a large bowl, add:

1	head red cabbage, sliced into thin strips
1	cucumber, peeled, sliced into thin round slices
1	cup pine nuts
2	vine ripened tomatoes, diced
1	avocado, cubed
½	cup extra virgin cold pressed olive oil
1	Jalapeño pepper, seeded, minced
2	tablespoons lemon juice
1	teaspoon sea salt

Mix well and serve.

SWEET KALE SALAD

time: 20 minutes

In a salad bowl, add:

1	head kale, remove stems by tearing off kale
$\frac{1}{4}$	cup extra virgin cold pressed olive oil
$\frac{1}{4}$	cup raw unheated honey
1	garlic clove, minced
$\frac{1}{2}$	cup raisins
2	tablespoons pine nuts

Use clean hands and massage ingredients for 5 minutes. By doing this, the kale softens and the flavors blend together.

TOP HAT TIP: "Raw" honey isn't necessarily unheated. Ask your supplier how it was processed.

HEARTY GREEN SALAD

time: 20 minutes

In a salad bowl, combine:

2	cups broccoli, chop crowns, grate stocks
2	cups red chard, chopped
$\frac{1}{2}$	cup walnuts, chopped
$\frac{1}{4}$	cup pumpkin seeds
$\frac{1}{4}$	sunflower seeds
1	cup mung bean sprouts*
$\frac{1}{2}$	cup lentil sprouts*

*See Sprouted Food chapter

Dressing

In a blender, add:

$\frac{1}{2}$	cup extra virgin cold pressed olive oil
1	avocado, pitted
1	tablespoon raw apple cider vinegar
3	tablespoons fresh lime juice
2	teaspoons crushed red pepper (if you like it hot)
$\frac{1}{4}$	cup fresh dill
1	teaspoon sea salt

Blend until creamy and pour over salad.

EVERYBODY'S FAVORITE SALAD

time: 20 minutes

In a salad bowl, combine:

2	large heads of romaine lettuce, wash and tear into small pieces
2	avocados, pitted and spooned into salad bowl
2	tomatoes, diced
1	tablespoon fresh lemon juice
2	teaspoons raw apple cider vinegar
3	tablespoons extra virgin cold pressed olive oil
1	teaspoon crushed red pepper (spice)
2	teaspoons sea salt
$\frac{1}{4}$	cup pine nuts
$\frac{1}{4}$	cup raisins

Mix ingredients together. Let sit for 10 minutes before serving.

GREEK SALAD

time: 25 minutes

In a salad bowl, combine:

2	small heads of Boston lettuce, wash and tear into small pieces
1	head red leaf lettuce, wash and tear into small pieces
3	vine ripened tomatoes, sliced into wedges
4	thin slices red onion
$\frac{1}{2}$	cucumber, peeled and chopped
10	raw Kalamata olives, pitted and chopped
3	scallions, diced
5	radishes, thinly sliced

Whisk together in separate bowl:

$\frac{1}{2}$	cup extra virgin cold pressed olive oil
2	tablespoons fresh lemon juice or raw apple cider vinegar
1	teaspoon finely minced garlic
1	tablespoon fresh oregano, minced
	Salt and ground pepper to taste

Pour dressing over salad and toss.

ITALIAN SALAD

time: 25 minutes

In a salad bowl, combine:

2	heads green leaf lettuce, washed and torn into small pieces.
8	cherry tomatoes, cut in half
1	cup fresh Italian parsley, finely chopped
$\frac{1}{4}$	cup leeks, chopped

Whisk together in a separate bowl:

$\frac{1}{4}$	cup fresh basil, chopped
$\frac{1}{4}$	cup fresh oregano, chopped
$\frac{1}{4}$	cup fresh sage, chopped
1	teaspoon sea salt
1	clove garlic, minced
2	tablespoons fresh lemon juice
$\frac{1}{2}$	cup extra virgin cold pressed olive oil

Pour dressing over salad and serve.

TOP HAT TIP: Use these recipes as guides. For example, if you don't have fresh sage but have parsley, try that. Be creative and see what works, and work with what you have.

ZUCCHINI SALAD

time: 15 minutes

In a salad bowl, add:

2	zucchini, peeled and grated
2	patty pan squash of your choice, peeled and diced
1	tablespoon green onion, diced
3	tablespoons extra virgin cold pressed olive oil
10	olives, whole pitted
1	teaspoon fresh ground pepper
2	tablespoons fresh lemon juice
1	teaspoon sea salt

Mix well and serve.

TOP HAT TIP: Look at labels when buying sea salt. You do not want salt that has been processed by heat, but rather naturally sun dried.

MEXICAN FOOD

For a great Mexican meal, we suggest one of these combinations:

Spanish Rice, Flax Seed 'Crunchy' Taco Shells or Flax Seed 'Crunchy' Tortillas, topped with Taco Meat, Salsa, Macho Nacho Sauce, and Guacamole.

Spanish Rice, Enchiladas, Macho Nacho Sauce or Fresh Tomatillo Sauce with Spinach, and Gazpacho Soup.

Nachos—Basic Flax Crackers (see Chips chapter) topped with Taco Meat, Macho Nacho Sauce, and Guacamole.

Taco Salad—chopped romaine lettuce topped with Taco Meat, Salsa, Macho Nacho Sauce, and Guacamole.

SALSA

time: 15 minutes

In a medium bowl, combine:

2	large ripe tomatoes, finely chopped
$\frac{1}{2}$	small red onion, finely chopped, rinsed, and drained
2	tablespoons fresh lemon juice
1	clove garlic, minced
$\frac{1}{4}$	cup fresh cilantro, chopped
1	Serrano pepper, minced, add to taste
1	teaspoon sea salt

Mix well and serve.

GUACAMOLE

time: 15 minutes

In a bowl, combine:

6	avocados, pitted (set aside 3 pits)
$\frac{1}{4}$	cup lime juice
$\frac{1}{2}$	cup cilantro, finely chopped
$\frac{1}{4}$	cup white onion, diced
1	vine ripened tomato, diced
1	Jalapeño pepper, minced
2	teaspoons sea salt or to taste

Mash ingredients together well. Add three avocado pits to prevent browning.

TOP HAT TIP: Avocados are a good fat, which is good for the body. Because fat takes more energy to digest, it is not recommended for those dealing with such challenges as cancer.

MACHO NACHO SAUCE

time: 10 minutes

In a blender, add:

$\frac{1}{2}$	cup distilled water
1	red bell pepper, washed and seeded
$\frac{1}{2}$	cup pine nuts
$\frac{1}{2}$	cup sunflower seeds
1	tablespoon miso (optional-if used omit sea salt) (Miso is a soy paste full of enzymes.)
1	clove garlic
1	tablespoon fresh lemon juice
1	Fresno pepper (red Jalapeño)
$1\frac{1}{2}$	teaspoons sea salt

Blend on high until creamy. Serve on top of tacos or as a dip for "*chips*."

TOP HAT TIP: A blender is needed for this recipe. The more powerful the better. We recommend the Vita-Mix® or the K-Tec® Champ.

SPANISH RICE

time: 20 minutes

In a salad bowl, combine:

1	head of cauliflower, grated in a food processor
4	green onions, diced
2	tomatoes, diced
1	orange bell pepper, diced
1	Jalapeño pepper, diced (optional, add if you like spicy food)
2	tablespoons fresh lemon juice
$\frac{1}{4}$	cup cilantro, diced
1	avocado (mashed in)
1	teaspoon chili powder
1	tablespoon paprika
$\frac{1}{2}$	tablespoon sea salt
$\frac{1}{4}$	cup cold pressed extra virgin olive oil

Mix together well and serve. As a side dish, serves four.
If Stephen is coming to dinner, serves one!

43

TACO MEAT

time: 10 minutes preparation
4 hours to soak

In a food processor using the S blade, add:

2   cups soaked walnuts, strain and discard water
1   tablespoon cumin powder
1   tablespoon coriander powder seasoning
1-2   tablespoons Nama Shoyu (raw soy sauce)
$\frac{1}{4}$ cup fresh cilantro
$\frac{1}{2}$ cup fresh cut corn (optional)

In the food processor, blend the ingredients until it looks like ground beef (about 15 seconds). Note: you might have to stop the machine and use a spoon to help mix the ingredients. Blend well.

To serve, place in cabbage, romaine, or Swiss chard leaves. For a special treat, serve in the Flax Seed "Crunchy" Taco Shells or Flax Seed 'Crunchy' Tortillas. Top with Salsa, Guacamole, and Macho Nacho Sauce (recipes in this chapter).

TOP HAT TIP: Soaking seeds and nuts releases enzyme inhibitors, making them easier to digest and promote health. Generally 4-8 hours is sufficient for seeds or 12-24 hours for nuts.

FLAX SEED 'CRUNCHY' TACO SHELLS or FLAX SEED 'CRUNCHY' TORTILLA

time: 1 hour preparation
18 hours to dehydrate

To prepare taco shells you will need plastic molds shaped like them. We improvised by using the corners of plastic $2\frac{1}{2}$ gallon water containers. They are made from food grade plastic, and we do not heat them above $100^\circ F$ in food preparation. For tortillas, no molds are necessary.

In a bowl, mix:

2   cups golden flax seeds, or brown flax seeds also work very well

2   cups distilled water

Let sit for 4 hours, then add:

2   tablespoons fresh lemon juice

$\frac{1}{2}$ tablespoon sea salt

Mix well. For taco shells, spread mixture into taco molds and dehydrate. For tortillas, spread mixture thinly into about 6" circles on a teflex sheet and dehydrate for about 18 hours.

(continued on next page)

FLAX SEED 'CRUNCHY' TACO SHELLS or FLAX SEED 'CRUNCHY' TORTILLAS (continued)

To serve Taco, put Taco Meat, Macho Nacho Sauce, Guacamole and Salsa in Flax Seed 'Crunchy' Taco Shells.

To serve Tostada, place these same toppings on Flax Seed 'Crunchy' Tortillas.

ENCHILADAS

time: 20 minutes preparation
2 hours to soak
12 hours to dehydrate

For this recipe you will also use the Taco Meat and Macho Nacho Sauce recipes.

Corn Shell
In a bowl, mix:

2	cups ground golden flax seeds soaked in 2 cups of water for 2 hours (this will become thick)
1	cup fresh cut corn creamed in a blender
2	tablespoons fresh lemon juice
	sea salt to taste

The ground flax/corn mixture should have a doughy consistency. Place a small handful of flax/corn mixture onto a dampened wooden cutting board. Using the bottom of a spoon, spread mixture into a small circle, similar to a corn tortilla. Place 3-4 tablespoons of Taco Meat on flattened flax/corn tortilla. Using a spatula to help raise the tortilla edge, roll the edge around the Taco Meat until completely covered. Place enchiladas on teflex dehydrating sheet and dehydrate for 12 hours at 98°F.

To serve, cover Enchiladas with Macho Nacho Sauce.

GAZPACHO SOUP

time: 25 minutes

In a large bowl, mix:

1	medium cucumber, peeled and chopped
1	medium zucchini, peeled and chopped
1	large green bell pepper, chopped
$\frac{1}{2}$	cup red onion, diced
$\frac{1}{2}$	cup fresh cilantro leaves, chopped
7	vine ripened tomatoes (5 coarsely chopped, 2 blended)
2	tablespoons raw apple cider vinegar
4	tablespoons extra virgin cold pressed olive oil
2	cloves garlic, minced
1	Fresno pepper (red Jalapeño), minced
1	cup fresh cut corn
2	teaspoons ground cumin
2	teaspoons fresh lime juice
2	teaspoons sea salt
1	avocado, cubed (optional)

Chill for 30 minutes and serve.

TOP HAT TIP: In the U.S. several foods (including canola, corn, flax, and soy beans) are genetically modified to withstand heavy chemical spraying to kill weeds and then sold without labeling. Organic food does not have toxic chemicals.

FRESH TOMATILLO SAUCE WITH SPINACH
time: 20 minutes

In blender, add:

    15-20 tomatillos (depending on their size)

    2   mild Jalapeño peppers, seeded

    3   cloves garlic

    2   large avocados, pitted and sliced

    2   teaspoons sea salt

    1   teaspoon ground black pepper

In a separate bowl, add:

    2   cups spinach, finely chopped

    $\frac{1}{2}$ cup scallions, finely chopped

    $\frac{1}{4}$ cup cilantro, finely chopped

Mix together and serve.

TOP HAT TIP: Large Jalapeño peppers are milder than the small ones.

NOTES

ITALIAN FOOD

For a delightful Italian supper, try the following combinations:

Rawviolis with Italian Salad (see Delicious Salads chapter).

Fettuccini *Not* Alfredo, Marinated Mushrooms, and Bread Sticks.

Spaghetti, Marinated Tomatoes, Bread Sticks.

Pizza with Everybody's Favorite Salad (see Delicious Salads chapter).

PIZZA

time: 30 minutes preparation
30 minutes to soak
14 hours to dehydrate

Crust

In a bowl, add:

½	cup golden flax seeds, ground in a coffee grinder
½	cup sunflower seeds, ground in a coffee grinder
2	tablespoons onion, minced
¾	cup distilled water

Mix well and let soak for 30 minutes. On a teflex dehydrator sheet, spread mixture in the shape of a pizza crust, about ¼ inch thick. Dehydrate for 7 hours. Remove from teflex sheet; turn over onto mesh dehydrator tray and dehydrate for another 7 hours.

(continued on next page)

PIZZA (continued)

Toppings

1	serving of Macho Nacho Sauce (found in the Mexican chapter). Note: we recommend you make this recipe with no salt. The Marinated Mushrooms will pick up the slack.)
1	serving Marinated Mushrooms (found on page 59, this chapter)
1	avocado, sliced
10	Sun Dried Tomatoes (in this chapter)
$\frac{1}{2}$	cup fresh basil
2	tablespoons fresh oregano

On the fully dehydrated pizza crust, add a thin layer of Macho Nacho Sauce, avocado slices, Sun Dried Tomatoes, Marinated Mushrooms, fresh basil and oregano.

BREAD STICKS

time: 30 minutes preparation
8 hours to soak
12 hours to dehydrate

In a food processor using the S blade, add:

- 1 cup barley soaked in 4 cups water, strain off water first
- 1 cup flax seed
- 1 cup carrot pulp (use pulp left over from juicing carrots)
- 1 tablespoon garlic powder
- 2 tablespoons extra virgin cold pressed olive oil
- 1 teaspoon sea salt
- $\frac{3}{4}$ cup water

Mix well; let mixture soak for 30 minutes. Roll dough into stick shape about 4 inches by 1 inch. Place on teflex sheet and dehydrate for 6 hours. Remove from teflex sheet; turn over onto mesh dehydrator tray and dehydrate for another 6 hours.

Variation: Sprinkle with sesame seeds before dehydrating.

TOP HAT TIP: For an easy way to transfer items from teflex sheets to mesh grid trays, place a clean mesh grid and tray over the items on the teflex sheet. Holding both trays securely, invert them. Carefully peel the teflex sheet away from items, using a spatula if necessary.

54

RAWVIOLI

time: 45 minutes preparation
8-9 hours to dehydrate

In a large bowl, marinate:

10	Roma tomatoes, thinly sliced
½	cup extra virgin cold pressed olive oil
3	garlic cloves minced
1	teaspoon sea salt

Marinate for at least 15 minutes.

Nut Cheese
Prepare by adding the following ingredients into blender:

1	cup of pine nuts (pinions)
½	cup sunflower seeds
½	tablespoon sea salt
¼	cup fresh basil
2	cloves garlic
½	cup distilled water

Place a paper towel underneath dehydrator screens to catch dripping liquid. Place one tomato slice on dehydrator screen. Add one spoonful of nut cheese on tomato slice. Top with another tomato slice. Repeat until all tomato slices are used. Dehydrate for 8-9 hours at 98° F.

FETTUCCINI *NOT* ALFREDO

time: 20 minutes

In a bowl, add:

5   large zucchini
2   Portobello mushrooms, diced

Use a potato peeler to remove the green skin from the zucchini; discard peel. Continue peeling the zucchini until reaching the zucchini's core; and save these peelings to serve as the pasta.

Not Alfredo Sauce
Place the following into blender:

3   vine ripened tomatoes
1   clove garlic
$\frac{1}{4}$ cup water
$\frac{1}{4}$ cup fresh oregano
$\frac{1}{4}$ cup fresh basil
1   tablespoon fresh rosemary
1-2   teaspoons cayenne pepper
1   tablespoon scallions
3   tablespoons extra virgin cold pressed olive oil
1   teaspoon sea salt

Blend sauce well. Pour sauce over zucchini peelings and mushrooms.

SPAGHETTI

time: 25 minutes

Pasta
In a bowl, add:

2	large zucchinis, which have been pealed and then grated in food processor
$\frac{1}{2}$	cup chopped mushrooms, use your favorite
6	Italian olives, pitted and halved

Sauce
In a blender, add:

2	cloves garlic
2	vine ripened tomatoes
$\frac{1}{2}$	cup Sun Dried Tomatoes (see recipe in this chapter)
2	tablespoons extra virgin cold pressed olive oil
$\frac{1}{4}$	cup fresh basil
$\frac{1}{4}$	cup fresh oregano
1	teaspoon sea salt

Blend well and pour over zucchini.

TOP HAT TIP: A Saladaco® is a manual device that makes spiral slices or angel hair strands out of vegetables.

<u>MARINATED TOMATOES</u>

time: 15 minutes

(The fresher the tomatoes, the better this recipe tastes!)

In a bowl, add:

6	vine ripened tomatoes, each sliced into 8 sections
4	cloves garlic, minced
1	Fresno pepper (red Jalapeño), minced
$\frac{1}{4}$	cup fresh basil, minced
1	teaspoon fresh rosemary, minced
1	cup extra virgin cold pressed olive oil

Let tomatoes marinate for about 10 minutes.

MARINATED MUSHROOMS

time: 35 minutes

In a bowl, add:

5	Shitake mushrooms, sliced
$\frac{1}{4}$	cup extra virgin cold pressed olive oil
$\frac{1}{4}$	cup Nama Shoyu (raw soy sauce)
$\frac{1}{2}$	teaspoon cayenne (optional)

Marinate for 30 minutes and serve.

TOP HAT TIP: Make a plan to eat healthier. For some its best to go one step at a time, others go for it 100%. If you find yourself reverting to old ways, just renew your plan!

SUN DRIED TOMATOES

time: 1 hour preparation
10 hours to dehydrate

In a large bowl, add:

10	Roma tomatoes, thinly sliced
$\frac{1}{2}$	cup extra virgin cold pressed olive oil
3	garlic cloves, minced
1	teaspoon onion powder
1	teaspoon sea salt

Marinate for at least 30 minutes. Place on teflex sheets and dehydrate for 5 hours, Remove from teflex sheet; turn over onto mesh dehydrator tray and dehydrate for another 5 hours. They should be chewy, not crunchy.

TOP HAT TIP: Be careful when using teflex sheets—do not use a sharp knife on them since they can be easily cut.

CHINESE FOOD

For a great Chinese dining experience, try one of these combos:

Fried Rice, Chinese Broccoli With Peanuts, and 3 Seaweeds And a Sea Bean Soup.

Fried Rice with Nori Rolls and Plum Sauce.

Chinese Broccoli With Peanuts, with Marinated Mushrooms. (see Italian chapter)

FRIED RICE

time: 10-15 minutes

In a salad bowl, combine:

3	cups burdock root, grated in a food processor
½	cup pea pods, chopped
1	medium carrot, chopped
¼	cup green onion, minced
1	tablespoon Nama Shoyu (raw soy sauce)
1	tablespoon Ume plum vinegar
1	avocado, mashed

Mix well and serve.

3 SEAWEEDS AND A SEA BEAN SOUP

time: 20 minutes

Seaweed Mixture

Combine in a large bowl:

1	cup dried laver, cut into 1 by 2 inch segments
1	cup dried dashi kombu, cut into 1 by 2 inch segments
1	cup dried kelp, cut into 1 by 2 inch segments
$\frac{1}{2}$	cup sea beans, chopped

Soup Broth

In a blender, add:

2	Jalapeño peppers
$\frac{1}{4}$	cup Nama Shoyu (raw soy sauce)
1	teaspoon ginger
1	clove garlic
$\frac{1}{4}$	cup chopped onion
4	cups water

Blend Soup Broth very well; pour soup broth over Seaweed Mixture and mix well. Let sit in refrigerator for 30 minutes.

TOP HAT TIP: You can find sea beans at well-stocked oriental stores.

CHINESE BROCCOLI WITH PEANUTS
time: 30 minutes

In a salad bowl, add:

3	cups broccoli tops, chopped
$\frac{1}{4}$	cup raw Spanish peanuts

In a blender, add:

1	Habañero pepper
1	clove garlic
$\frac{1}{4}$	cup extra virgin cold pressed olive oil
$\frac{1}{4}$	cup pine nuts
$\frac{1}{2}$	avocado
1	tablespoon fresh lemon juice
1	teaspoon salt

Blend until creamy, pour over broccoli and peanuts. Let marinate for 45 minutes in the refrigerator.

PLUM SAUCE

time: 20 minutes

Soak 2 cups of unsulfured prunes in 2 cups of water for 10 minutes.

In a blender, add:

2	cups of soaked prunes, strain and discard water
1	teaspoon minced ginger root
1	tablespoon raw apple cider vinegar
$\frac{1}{4}$	cup water
2	teaspoons minced Jalapeño pepper

Blend until creamy. Goes great with Nori Rolls.

NORI ROLLS

time: 25 minutes

In a large bowl, add:

$\frac{1}{2}$ cup mung bean sprouts

$\frac{1}{2}$ cup carrot, grated

1 teaspoon minced ginger root

1 avocado, mashed

1 tablespoon Nama Shoyu (raw soy sauce)

Mix ingredients well. Wrap ingredients in raw nori sheets. Dip finger in a bowl of water and wet the nori. Moisture allows it to slide well.

TOP HAT TIP: You can really get creative with what you wrap in a nori roll. Don't eat and run, roll and eat.

PROVERB COOKIES

time: 20 minutes preparation
2 hours to soak
11-12 hours to dehydrate

In a large bowl, add:

1	cup freshly ground whole wheat flour
2	cups golden flax seeds
½	cup unheated honey
¼	cup extra virgin cold pressed olive oil
1	teaspoon sea salt
1	cup distilled water

Mix ingredients well. Shape into 3½ inch circles on teflex sheets and dehydrate for 1 hour at 98 F.° Next fold in half and then in half again like a fortune cookie. Dehydrate for 11-12 hours.

TOP HAT TIP: Have fun hiding your favorite Proverbs inside the fortune cookies.

NOTES

MEDITERRANEAN FOOD

For a tasty Mediterranean dinner, try one of these
combinations:

Greek Salad (see Delicious Salads chapter), Hummus,
Wraps.

Tabouleh, Hummus, and Baklava .

For a tasty snack try Hummus with Basic Flax Chips
(see Chips chapter).

HUMMUS

time: 20 minutes

In a food processor using the S blade, add:

2	cloves garlic
1	zucchini, peeled and chopped
2	cups sunflower seeds
$\frac{1}{2}$	cup raw tahini
$\frac{1}{4}$	cup fresh lemon juice
1/3	cup distilled water
1/3	cup extra virgin cold pressed olive oil
2	teaspoons sea salt

Mix in the food processor on high until creamy.

TOP HAT TIP: Distilled water is preferred as a first choice, second would be filtered, to help remove impurities in tap water.

TABOULEH

time: 20 minutes

In a large bowl, add:

$\frac{1}{4}$	cup onion, finely chopped
4	cups parsley, finely chopped
$\frac{1}{4}$	cup extra virgin cold pressed olive oil
1	clove garlic, minced
2	tablespoons fresh lemon juice
2	teaspoons sea salt

Enjoy!

TOP HAT TIP: Extra virgin olive oil is the first pressing of the olives, having the highest availability of the good ingredients. When it is cold pressed, the ingredients are preserved.

BAKLAVA

time: 30 minutes preparation
4 hours to soak

In a food processor using the S blade, add:

3	cups walnuts, soaked for 4 hours and drained
$\frac{1}{2}$	cup raw unheated honey
3	cups hazelnuts
15	large dates, pitted
2	tablespoons coconut butter (optional)

Flatten layers in pan and serve.

TOP HAT TIP: If you are like us and decide what to make for dinner at 5 PM, then this tip is for you. Ahead of time, soak and rinse a big batch of raw nuts, then dehydrate them. This way you'll always have "soaked nuts" on hand.

WRAPS

time: 30 minutes preparation
8 hours to soak

Pâté
In a food processor using the S blade, add:

$\frac{1}{4}$ cup red cabbage

2   cups spelt, soaked in 3 cups of water for 8 hours, strain and discard water

2   tablespoons extra virgin cold pressed olive oil

3   tablespoons fresh lemon juice

1   teaspoon sea salt

Process for 30 seconds or until it is smooth like a pâté.

Mixed Vegetables
In a bowl, add:

1   cup cauliflower, chopped

1   cup broccoli, chopped

2   tablespoons extra virgin cold pressed olive oil

2   teaspoons paprika

    sea salt to taste (optional)

Mix well. Spread the pâté on a red chard leaf and top with mixed vegetables.

NOTES

AMERICAN FOOD

Yummy American-style combinations:

Raw Roasted Almonds and Honey Nuts are always a tasty snack to have handy.

Corn Dog, Ketchup, Coleslaw, and Carmel Apple.

Philly Cheese Steak with Everybody's Favorite Salad (see Delicious Salads chapter).

BLT...S/A with Cranberry Salad and a Carmel Apple (if you are in a sweet mood).

ALMOND MILK

time: 10 minutes preparation
6 hours to soak

Soak 1 cup of raw almonds in 2 cups of water for at least 6 hours.

In a blender, add:

1   cup presoaked almonds, water drained
4   cups distilled water

Blend on high until creamy. Strain milk through fine strainer or cheese cloth to remove fiber. Keeps 2-5 days in refrigerator.

Chill and serve.

Variation: To sweeten, add honey or a few pitted dates and blend, or add raw carob powder and you have "chocolate milk."

TOP HAT TIP: Nuts change from about 25% protein and 75% fat to about 75% protein and 25% fat when sprouted.

BACON, WHY NOT?

time: 30 minutes preparation
2 hours to marinate
18 hours to dehydrate

In a bowl, marinate:

1	large eggplant, thinly sliced length wise
$\frac{3}{4}$	cup extra virgin cold pressed olive oil
1	teaspoon ground black pepper
2	tablespoons unheated honey
4	tablespoons Ume Plum Vinegar

Marinate for 2 hours, place on teflex sheets and dehydrate for 9 hours. Turn "bacon" over and dehydrate for another 9 hours. Bacon should be crispy.

BLT...S/A (Sprouts/Avocado)

time: 20 minutes

Needed: 1 Bacon, Why Not? recipe

Prepare:

1	head romaine lettuce; cut off bottom and wash—don't chop—use the whole leaves
1	vine ripened tomato, sliced
1	cup alfalfa sprouts
1	avocado, pitted and sliced

On a leaf of romaine place a strip of bacon, a slice of tomato, avocado and alfalfa sprouts. Roll the leaf and eat.

Tastes great!

COLESLAW

time: 20 minutes

In a bowl, add:

1	head green cabbage, shredded
1	cucumber, peeled and diced
1	cup pineapple, chopped
1	Jalapeño pepper, minced

In a blender, add:

$\frac{1}{4}$	cup extra virgin cold pressed olive oil
1	avocado, remove pit
2	tablespoons pine nuts
1	tablespoon raw apple cider vinegar
2	teaspoons celery seed
1	teaspoon sea salt

Blend well and pour over slaw.

Variation: Use caraway seed instead of celery seed with fresh lemon juice instead of raw apple cider vinegar.

TOP HAT TIP: It is best not to combine fruit with vegetables. So as taste buds appreciate new flavors, try to avoid the combination.

KETCHUP

Presoak 1 cup of Sun Dried Tomatoes in 3 cups distilled water for 15-20 minutes. Drain water once the Sun Dried Tomatoes feel re-hydrated.

In a blender, add:

1	cup presoaked Sun Dried Tomatoes
2	tablespoons raw apple cider vinegar
$\frac{1}{2}$	cup of Medjool dates, remove pits
1	pear, peeled and cored
1	vine ripened tomato, remove stem
$\frac{1}{2}$-1	cup of distilled water (depending on how thick you prefer your Ketchup)
1-2	teaspoons sea salt

Blend well and serve. Keep refrigerated up to 3 days.

CORN DOG

time: 1 hour preparation
1 hour to soak
12 hours to dehydrate

In a coffee grinder, grind:

2   cups golden flax seeds

Soak ground flax seeds in 2 cups of distilled water until sticky (about 15 minutes). While soaking, we recommend for times sake that you prepare the Raw Dog (see next page) and then return and prepare the Corn Bread Shell.

Corn Bread Shell
In a blender, add:

2   cups fresh corn

Blend until creamy.

In a bowl, add:

     presoaked ground flax seeds
2   cups blended corn
1   tablespoon raw unheated honey
1   teaspoon sea salt

Mix ingredients well and set aside.

(continued on next page)

CORN DOG (continued)

In a food processor using the S blade, add:

1	cup walnuts
1	cup pine nuts
½	cup parsley
1	cup celery
1	clove garlic
½	red bell pepper
1	Jalapeño pepper
1	tablespoon cumin
1	teaspoon tarragon
1	teaspoon sea salt

Process completely.

The ground flax/corn mixture should have a doughy consistency. Place a small handful of the flax/corn mixture onto a dampened cutting board. Using the bottom of a spoon, spread the mixture into a small circle similar to a corn tortilla. Place 3-4 tablespoons of Raw Dog dough on flattened flax/corn tortilla. Using a spatula to help raise the tortilla edge, roll the edge around the Raw Dog until completely covered. Place Corn Dog on teflex dehydrating sheet and dehydrate until hard, about 12 hours at 98°F. To finish Corn Dog, place a Popsicle stick in one end.

PHILLY CHEESESTEAK

time: 45 minutes

Steak
In a bowl, add:

2	Portobello mushrooms, sliced
½	cup extra virgin cold pressed olive oil
½	cup Nama Shoyu (raw soy sauce)
2	teaspoons cumin powder
2	teaspoons coriander powder
1	tablespoon Ume plum vinegar

Set aside and let marinate.

Vegetables
In a separate bowl, add:

1	green bell pepper, seeded and sliced
1	cup broccoli, chopped
½	cup white onion, chopped
1	clove garlic, minced
1	teaspoon sea salt
¼	cup extra virgin cold pressed olive oil

Set aside and let marinate.

(continued on next page)

 83

<u>PHILLY CHEESESTEAK</u> (continued)

<u>Cheese</u>
In a blender, add:

1	cup pine nuts
$\frac{1}{2}$	cup sunflower seeds
2-3	tablespoons raw apple cider vinegar
$\frac{1}{4}$	cup onion
1	teaspoon sea salt
$\frac{1}{4}$	cup distilled water

Blend until creamy.

To make the Philly Cheesesteak, start with a whole Swiss chard leaf. First spread a layer of steak, then the vegetables, and finally the cheese. Roll and eat!

CARAMEL APPLE

time: 20 minutes

In a food processor using the S blade, add:

$1\frac{1}{2}$	cup hazelnuts
$\frac{3}{4}$	cup dates
$\frac{1}{4}$	cup raw unheated honey
2	tablespoons raw carob powder

Process until like paste. Place apple on a Popsicle stick and cover apple with paste.

Variation: Roll in coconut.

CRANBERRY SALAD

time: 20 minutes

In a blender, add:

1	cup cranberries
1	cup dates, pitted and soaked in 2 cups of water for 10 minutes, strain and discard water
$\frac{1}{2}$	teaspoon allspice
2	teaspoons cinnamon
$\frac{1}{2}$	teaspoon ground cloves
2	teaspoons coconut butter

Blend together well.

In a separate bowl, add.

2	pears, cored and chopped
2	apples, cored and chopped
1	cup pineapple, chopped
1	cup chopped walnuts or pecans
$\frac{1}{2}$	cup raisins

Pour blender contents over fruit and mix well. Great to serve at Thanksgiving and Christmas for dinner.

TOP HAT TIP: Coconut butter may be purchased at <u>Nature's First Law</u> at www.rawfood.com.

86

CRANBERRY BREAD

time: 20 minutes preparation
8 hours to dehydrate

In a food processor using the S blade, add:

1	cup cranberries
1	apple, cored and chopped
1	orange, peeled and seeded
1	tablespoon cinnamon
4	tablespoons raw unheated honey

Process until finely ground.

Place in a mixing bowl and add:

2	cups walnuts, coarsely chopped
1	cup freshly ground whole wheat flour

Mix ingredients well, spread mixture $\frac{1}{4}$ inch thick on a 14"
by 14" teflex sheet and score into 2-inch squares.
Dehydrate for 4 hours. Remove from teflex sheet; turn
over onto mesh dehydrator tray and dehydrate for another
4 hours. Almond butter and honey taste great on this
bread.

RAW ROASTED ALMONDS

time: 10 minutes preparation
14 hours to dehydrate

In a <u>container with a lid</u>, add:

3	cups almonds
2	garlic cloves, pressed
4	teaspoons sea salt
2	tablespoons UDO's CHOICE® Perfected Oil Blend
1	tablespoon fresh lemon juice

With lid on container, shake well to mix all the ingredients together. Place nuts on teflex sheets in a dehydrator for 14 hours.

HONEY NUTS

time: 15 minutes preparation
15 hours to dehydrate

In a bowl, add:

1	cup walnuts, chopped
1	cup almonds chopped
1	cup brazil nuts, chopped
½	cup raw unheated honey
1	tablespoon raw carob powder

Mix ingredients well, and dehydrate for 15 hours.

<u>NOTES</u>

JUICES

STRAIGHT-UP CHUGGIN'

In a juicer, add:

$\frac{1}{2}$ bunch dandelion
$\frac{1}{2}$ bunch collard greens
$\frac{1}{2}$ bunch dinosaur kale
$\frac{1}{2}$ bunch arugula
$\frac{1}{2}$ head bok choy
(add some apple if you can't handle the bitterness)

This juice was so named because of its potency and flavor. Although this drink is probably the most nutritious combination you can put in your body, sipping is not recommended. And remember, *"The more bitter, the more better."*

STRAIGHT SIPPIN'

In a juicer, add:

4	vine ripened tomatoes
4	ribs celery
2	cloves garlic
1-2	Jalapeño peppers
$\frac{1}{4}$	bunch cilantro

Mix in juice:

1	teaspoon sea salt
$\frac{1}{4}$	cup extra virgin cold pressed olive oil

This juice is always nice when you are juice fasting, although we guess anything tastes good on a juice fast.

GREEN PINEAPPLE

In a juicer, add:

1	bunch parsley
4	ribs celery
$\frac{1}{2}$	pineapple

THE DANDY APPLE

In a juicer, add:

1	bunch red dandelion
3	red delicious apples
$\frac{1}{2}$	red bell pepper
$\frac{1}{2}$	inch cube ginger root

COOL Q

In a juicer, add:

1	cucumber
1	head romaine lettuce
2	cups grapes
$\frac{1}{2}$	lemon

UNTO THINE OWN LIVER BE TRUE

In a juicer, add:

1	bunch spinach
$\frac{1}{4}$	beet
$\frac{1}{2}$	lemon
1	cucumber

LEMON LIME SPARKLE

In a juicer, add:

- 1   cup spring water (fresh spring if you live near a natural spring)
- ½   lemon
- ½   lime, remove skin with paring knife
- 2   green pears

PLASMA

In a juicer, add:

- ½   lemon
- 2   pears
- ¼   pineapple
- 1   inch cube ginger root
- 1   cup red grapes

MORNING BERRY

In a juicer, add:

- 1   cup strawberries
- 1   cup blueberries
- 4   oranges (peel skin; leave white membrane on)

ROOT N' FRUIT

In a juicer, add:

3	feet burdock root
5	kiwi, remove skins
2	apples

SUMMER REFRESHER

In a juicer, add:

$\frac{1}{4}$	medium size watermelon, including rind
3	peaches, pitted

SMOOTHIES

STRAWBERRY SUNRISE SURPRISE

In a blender, add:

2	bananas, peeled
1	apple
1	pear
10	frozen strawberries
1	cup Almond Milk (see American chapter)
$\frac{1}{4}$	cup pine nuts

Blend until smooth.

CITRUS SPRITZ

In a blender, add:

2	frozen bananas
1	cup fresh squeezed orange juice
2	golden kiwis
$\frac{1}{2}$	cup fresh pineapple
$\frac{1}{4}$	cup almonds

Blend until smooth.

VERY BERRY SPLASH

In a blender, add:

1	cup fresh apple juice
1	banana
½	cup blueberries
½	cup blackberries
½	cup raspberries
10	strawberries, frozen

Blend until smooth.

PEENYA KOWLADA

In a blender, add:

2	frozen bananas
1	young coconut, juice and meat
½	cup macadamia nuts
1	cup fresh pineapple

Blend until smooth.

TOP HAT TIP: Keep young coconuts handy. The chemical composition is only a few molecules different than your blood's plasma.

POWER SMOOTHIE

In a blender, add:

2	bananas
1	young coconut, juice and meat
1	tablespoon of dehydrated barley juice powder
1	cup sunflower seed sprouts
½	cup dates, pitted

Blend until smooth.

Note: For information on ordering the dehydrated barley juice powder call 1-888-661-7401.

SCARY CHERRY

In a blender, add:

2	bananas
1	cup apple juice
1	cup cherries, pitted
½	cup blueberries
½	cup pine nuts
½	vanilla bean

Blend until smooth.

THE FAT LOVER

In a blender, add:

2	frozen bananas
1	cup durian (Asian fruit)
½	cup almond milk
1	young coconut, juice and meat
¼	cup pumpkin seeds
¼	cup Brazil nuts
¼	cup Macadamia nuts
¼	cup hemp seeds
1	tablespoon coconut butter

Blend until creamy.

MANGO TANGO

In a blender, add:

1	cup Almond Milk
1	cup mango
1	cup peaches
½	cup raw cashews
1	tablespoon raw unheated honey

Blend until smooth.

SOUR POWER

In a blender, add:

2	bananas
$\frac{3}{4}$	cup fresh squeezed orange juice
$\frac{1}{4}$	cup fresh lemon juice
$\frac{1}{2}$	cup raspberries
10	frozen strawberries
1	green apple
1	tablespoon raw unheated honey

Blend until smooth.

STONE-FRUIT SMOOTHIE

In a blender, add:

1	cup fresh pear juice (pre-juice the pears)
1	peach, pitted
1	nectarine, pitted
3	apricots, pitted

Blend until smooth.

TOP HAT TIP: Too many smoothies are high in sugar and can cause imbalance in the body. Use as an occasional treat or to help refuel after strenuous exercise.

CHIPS

BASIC FLAX CHIPS

time: 45 minutes preparation
2 hours to soak
10-13 hours to dehydrate

In a large bowl, add:

2 cups golden flax seeds
1-1$\frac{1}{2}$ cups distilled water
3 tablespoons fresh lemon juice
2 teaspoons sea salt

Mix well and let soak for 2 hours.

Spread flax mixture onto teflex dehydrator sheets and shape thinly into small chips. Dehydrate for 10-13 hours at 98°F.

POTATO CHIPS

time: 20 minutes preparation
2-3 hours to soak
11-12 hours to dehydrate

In a bowl, add:

6   red potatoes, thinly sliced (if you use Russet
       potatoes, trim off any green spots)
5   cups distilled water

Soak about 2-3 hours; rinse and drain to remove starch.

In a clean bowl, add:

       potato slices
¼   cup extra virgin cold pressed olive oil
¼   cup Ume Plum Vinegar (or raw apple cider
       vinegar and sea salt)
1   teaspoon cayenne pepper
       sea salt to taste

Marinate for 1 hour. Place each chip on teflex sheet and
dehydrate 11-12 hours at 98°F.

TOP HAT TIP: Use a mandoline (a manually operated hand held
slicing tool) for ease in fine slicing or making julienne strips. Handle
with care, as the blades are very sharp.

APPLE CINNAMON YAM CHIPS

time: 25 minutes preparation
2-3 hours to soak
11-12 hours to dehydrate

In a bowl, add:

3	yams, peeled and thinly sliced
5	cups distilled water

Soak for 2 hours. Strain water

In a clean bowl, add:

	yam slices
3	tablespoons cold pressed coconut butter
1	tablespoon cinnamon
$\frac{1}{2}$	cup freshly juiced apple juice

Marinate for 1 hour. Place each chip on teflex sheet and dehydrate for 11-12 hours at 98°F.

SPICY SALSA CHIPS

time: 15 minutes preparation
3-4 hours to soak
12-15 hours to dehydrate

In a blender, add:

3	vine ripened tomatoes
3	Serrano peppers
3	tomatillos
3	tablespoons fresh lemon juice
1	clove garlic
$\frac{1}{4}$	cup cilantro
1	teaspoon sea salt
$\frac{1}{4}$	cup distilled water

Blend well.

In a large bowl, add:

2	cups brown flax seeds

Pour blended salsa mixture over flax seeds and stir together. Soak for 3-4 hours in refrigerator. Spoon small portions of soaked flax seeds onto teflex dehydrator sheet and shape into chips. Dehydrate for 12-15 hours at 98°F.

NOTES

SPROUTED FOOD

SPROUTS

Not only are sprouts affordable and convenient, but they are a great source of nutrition. Whether you buy your sprouts or sprout them yourself, be aware that they are always susceptible to molding that can make you sick. Go easy when you first start sprouting, because we have found that there is usually an adjustment period before the stomach can handle the concentrated nutrition. On the next page is a beginner chart that tells you the times required for sprouting various seeds and beans. Sprouting time varies depending on humidity in your area.

Step 1- To kill mold: Mix 1/3 part hydrogen peroxide (3% grade) with 2/3 part water. Pour over nuts, seeds, or grains. Soak 10-20 minutes. Bubbling action signifies mold. Rinse thoroughly.

Step 2- Soak nuts, seeds, or grains in purified water.

Step 3- Drain water and store container in a dark place. rinse nuts, seeds, or grains every 6-10 hours.

Step 4- Once sprouted, refrigerate for up to 3 days.

SPROUTING GUIDE

Things to sprout	Soaking Time (Hours)	Days to Sprout*
Adzuki bean	12	3-5
Alfalfa	8	3-5
Barley (sproutable)	10	3-5
Buckwheat groats	10	3-5
Chick peas (garbanzo beans)	10	4-6
Lentil (any color)	8	2-4
Mung bean	12	2-4
Pea	12	3-5
Quinoa	8	3-5
Radish	8	3-5
Rye berries	10	2-4
Sesame seeds	6	2-4
Soybean	8	3-5
Sunflower seeds (hulled)	8	2-4
Wheat	8	3-5
Wild Rice	10	5-8

*Sprouts are ready when a tail is noticeable.

SPROUTS TO GO

time: 10 minutes preparation
2-4 days to sprout

In a bowl, add:

½	cup lentil sprouts
½	cup mung bean sprouts
1	cup cabbage, chopped
1	Jalapeño pepper, chopped
2	tablespoons extra virgin cold pressed olive oil
2	teaspoons fresh lemon juice
1	teaspoon dried oregano
1	avocado, cubed
2	teaspoons sea salt

Mix well and eat.

GET UP 'N GO GRAINS

time: 15 minutes preparation
3-5 days to sprout

In a bowl, add:

$\frac{1}{2}$	cup wheat or barley, sprouted
$\frac{1}{2}$	cup rye berries, sprouted
$\frac{1}{2}$	cup sunflower seeds, sprouted
1	banana, peeled and sliced
$\frac{1}{2}$	cup blueberries
$\frac{1}{2}$	cup raspberries
$\frac{1}{2}$	cup blackberries
5	dates, pitted and chopped

Great to eat with Almond Milk. (see American chapter)

GOES DOWN EZ...SOUP

time: 30 minutes preparation
5-8 days to sprout

In a large bowl add:

$\frac{1}{4}$	cup mung bean sprouts (sprout your own or buy)
$\frac{1}{4}$	cup red lentils, sprouted
$\frac{1}{4}$	cup adzuki beans, sprouted
$\frac{1}{4}$	cup wild rice, sprouted
2	tomatoes, diced
1	cup corn, freshly cut
2	cups cucumber, peeled and chopped
1	avocado, diced

In a blender, add:

3	tomatoes
1-2	garlic cloves, minced
1	Fresno pepper (red Jalapeño), minced
$\frac{1}{4}$	cup fresh oregano
$\frac{1}{4}$	cup fresh dill weed
2	teaspoons sea salt

Blend until chunky and mix with other ingredients.

SCIENCE FICTION SALAD
...it's out of this world
time: 25 minutes preparation

Salad

1	head Boston lettuce, torn
1	head red leaf lettuce, torn
3	Brussels sprouts, shredded
$\frac{1}{2}$	cup pea sprouts*
$\frac{1}{2}$	cup sunflower seed sprouts*
$\frac{1}{2}$	cup broccoli sprouts*
$\frac{1}{2}$	cup radish sprouts*
$\frac{1}{2}$	cup clover sprouts*
2	nectarines, pitted and chopped

*Buy green sprouts at store.

Dressing

In a blender add:

1	cup filtered water
$\frac{1}{2}$	avocado
1	tablespoon Umeboshi Paste
1	tablespoon raw unheated honey

Blend until creamy. Pour over salad.

NOTES

DESSERTS

UNIVERSAL PIE CRUST

time: 15 minutes

In a food processor using the S blade, add:

    2   cups hazelnuts
    2   cups dates, pitted (presoak in 3 cups of
           water for 10 minutes before putting them in the
           food processor; discard water)

We have found that the combination of the hazelnuts with dates works best for any pie crust.

Process nuts and dates until it has a thick dough-like consistency. Press in a pie pan. Make sure not to eat all the crust when taste testing!

LEMON TART PIE

time: 25 minutes

2 hours to freeze

Needed: 1 Universal Pie Crust

In a blender, add:

5	apple bananas
$\frac{1}{4}$	cup fresh lemon juice
$\frac{1}{4}$	cup raw unheated honey
3	tablespoons psyllium powder
$\frac{1}{2}$	cup pine nuts

Blend until creamy.

Pour into Universal Pie Crust. Store in freezer for 1-2 hours, then serve.

__TOP HAT TIP__: Psyllium powder is a thickener and a binder.

DATE BALL TREATS

time: 20 minutes

In a food processor using the S blade, add:

$\frac{1}{2}$ cup almonds
$\frac{1}{2}$ cup sunflower seeds

Be careful not to burn out the motor—process until almonds and sunflower seeds are finely ground.

Next, add:

1   cup dates, pitted and soaked in water for 10 minutes (discard water).
1   vanilla bean, clip off both ends
2   tablespoons raw unheated honey
2   tablespoons raw carob powder

Process until everything is well ground. Wash your hands! Use your hands to roll the mixture into balls, the size of a golf ball.

TOP HAT TIP: Add 4-5 drops of Peppermint Extract for an alternative Peppermint taste. Great for Mexican desserts and Christmas treats.

BYE BYE REAL APPLE PIE

time: 30 minutes

Needed: 1 Universal Pie Crust

In a gallon size zip-lock bag, add:

5	gala apples, peeled, cored, and sliced as thin as possible
$\frac{1}{2}$	cup raisins
1	tablespoon cinnamon
2	tablespoons raw unheated honey
1	teaspoon allspice

With bag closed, massage ingredients for about 5 minutes or until the apples begin to break down. Pour contents into pie crust and serve.

Goes great with "Ice Cream" (in this chapter).

TOP HAT TIP: Inorganic grapes are heavily sprayed with chemicals. By dehydrating inorganic grapes, called raisins, the chemicals are concentrated in the dried fruit. We recommend using organic raisins.

STRAWBERRY PIE

time: 1 hour

Needed: 1 Universal Pie Crust

Filling

3 cups strawberries, remove green tops and slice berries in half

Place sliced strawberries in pie shell.

Glaze

In a blender, place:

$\frac{1}{2}$ cup strawberries, remove green tops
$\frac{1}{4}$ cup raw unheated honey
$\frac{1}{2}$ cup coconut milk, from young coconut
3 tablespoons psyllium powder

Blend until creamy.

Pour glaze over strawberries and chill for 30 minutes.

TOP HAT TIP: To open a coconut, jab the bottom with a screw driver until you find the weak spot; and drain out the liquid for a recipe or to drink. (Yummy!) Hit coconut hard on concrete until it splits open, and eat fresh or dehydrate the flesh for a snack. Option: Cut open with cleaver or very strong knife.

TASTY TROPICAL PIE

time: 45 minutes

Needed: 1 Universal Pie Crust

In a blender, add:

3	apple bananas
1	mango, peeled and pitted (good luck, there's no easy way)
1	young coconut flesh, without coconut milk
1	cup pineapple
2	tablespoons raw unheated honey
2	tablespoons psyllium seed powder

Blend until creamy. Pour into Universal Pie Crust.

Topping (optional)

3   kiwis

For a beautiful topping, peel and thinly slice 3 kiwis. Place in refrigerator to chill.

TOP HAT TIP: To get the flesh of a mango: Cut to the seed around the flattest perimeter. Then slice one half as close to the seed as possible. Score the flesh and turn "inside out," and cut away the peel. Cut the seed away from the other section. GOOD LUCK, there is no easy way.

ICE CREAM

time: 1 hour

Needed: 1 ice cream maker, rock salt, and ice.

In a blender, add

6	cups almond milk
1	vanilla bean, clip off ends
1	cup dates, pitted
$\frac{1}{2}$	cup raw unheated honey
$\frac{1}{4}$	cup cold pressed coconut butter or UDO's CHOICE® Perfected Oil Blend

Blend until smooth. Freeze according to ice cream maker directions.

The above ingredients are how we start all of our ice creams. You can add any sweet fruit in any amount that you prefer after that. Stephen's favorite addition is peaches while Charles' favorite is carob-mint (raw carob powder and mint herb).

WHEN RAW?
Daily and Special Occasions, all the time
Social Events / Potlucks

Planning social events to associate with others who want to improve their health, is a great way to be encouraged on the raw food diet. The Top Raw Men™ created a monthly raw food potluck called "Youthful Longevity." It started out to be only for youth, but quickly expanded to include people of all ages. They have a theme for each potluck where everyone brings a food item to correspond with the theme. Themes have included Mexican, Italian, Hawaiian, Favorites, Picnic/Outdoor Foods, and Smoothies. It has been exciting to see people's creativity in raw food preparation. The women usually like the colorful food presentations, while the men just like the great tasting food. The potlucks start with a game for a social mixer, and the winning team eats first. After eating and socializing, the "icing on the cake" is a featured speaker who talks on any health issue (juicing, cleansing, exercise, etc., or their personal testimony of health improvements with the diet).

Here are some themes and games that have proved to be very successful.

THEMES FOR SOCIALS

January- Italian food.

February- Valentine month. Have foods that are sweet in nature, red in color, or shaped like a heart.

March- American food.

April- Everybody's favorite foods.

May- Cinco de Mayo- Mexican food.

June- Hawaiian Luau- Use tropical fruits and vegetables.

July- 4th of July, patriotic theme. Outdoor and picnic food.

August- Southwestern Barbeque / Cowboy food.

September- Mediterranean food.

October- Chinese food.

November- Thanksgiving food. Be creative in substituting raw food nourishing ingredients for the "normal" ones.

December- Christmas theme. Everything from dinner menu to snacks and candies. Use bell and tree shapes, etc.

Have fun!

FUN GAMES FOR SOCIALS

Here are some fun "food games" to get people thinking about different types of food. Many people's diets only consist of meat, potatoes, and a few familiar vegetables. These games expand their horizon of the veggie world.

CUT UP GAME

Game - Split into even teams. Give each team a plastic knife and large vegetable or fruit. Use seasonal items. Bananas, squash, pumpkins, etc. The goal is to shape the vegetable or fruit into something that represents the theme of the potluck. Have fun and be creative. No pumpkin faces allowed, that is too easy. Ten minutes is usually enough time.

MEET THE BODY Quiz

1. Memorize or learn by _____
2. The teacher and the _____
3. You must _____ the music
4. _____ in the family closet
5. By word of _____
6. The way of all _____
7. Take it on the _____
8. Of all the _____
9. By the _____ of your teeth
10. You should _____ the mark
11. _____ is thicker than water
12. The _____ of the land
13. _____ your way through a crowd
14. Out on a _____
15. Sinking your _____ into a problem
16. _____the lion in his den
17. Putting your best _____ forward
18. _____ down to work
19. An itching _____
20. _____ _____ hooray
21. Lend me your _____
22. By the hair of your _____ _____ _____
23. 'Twist the cup and _____'
24. _____ of the loaf of bread
25. Just follow your _____

26. _____ and crossbones
27. The fatted _____
28. _____ the favorite in a race
29. A _____ of silver in ore
30. Listed in the _____ in the back of the book
31. Let's give him a great big _____
32. _____ high to a grasshopper
33. Tease or _____ your friends
34. Give the cold _____
35. A rule of _____
36. New idea or latest _____
37. _____ by jowl
38. By the sweat of his _____
39. In the _____ of luxury
40. Put it in your hope _____
41. This is the bottle _____
42. Keystone of the _____
43. Eating _____ beans
44. Hit the _____ on the head

MEET THE BODY ANSWERS

1. HEART
2. PUPIL
3. FACE
4. SKELETON
5. MOUTH
6. FLESH
7. CHIN
8. NERVE
9. SKIN
10. TOE
11. BLOOD
12. FAT
13. ELBOW
14. LIMB
15. TEETH
16. BEARD
17. FOOT
18. KNUCKLE
19. PALM

20. HIP HIP
21. EAR
22. CHINNY CHIN CHIN
23. LIPS
24. HEEL
25. NOSE
26. SKULL
27. CALF
28. BACK
29. VEIN
30. APPENDIX
31. HAND
32. KNEE
33. RIB
34. SHOULDER
35. THUMB
36. WRINKLE
37. CHEEK
38. BROW

39. LAP
40. CHEST
41. NECK
42. ARCH
43. KIDNEY
44. NAIL

NAME THAT PLANT

A portion of the name of a fruit or vegetable is missing. What is it?

Question	Answers
1. egg	eggplant
2. cab	cabbage
3. flower	cauliflower
4. collar	collards
5. dish	radish
6. ant	cantaloupe
7. pump	pumpkin
8. ash	squash
9. spin	spinach
10. choke	artichoke
11. chest	water chestnut
12. range	orange
13. pay	papaya
14. ear	pear
15. cot	apricot
16. honey	honeydew
17. tar	nectarine
18. raw	strawberry
19. hub	rhubarb
20. ban	banana
(Bonus point) term	watermelon

NAME THAT FRUIT
(suggestion: use at a Hawaiian Luau)

Match the following questions with the answers listed below. Who am I?

1. I am both stunning and delicious. My ribs are prominent and a glossy yellow. My skin is thin, waxy, and edible. My taste likens to a flowery combination of plums, McIntosh apples and Concord grapes, with a touch of citrus.

2. I am often confused with my cousin, feijoa, but I am my own fruit! I am egg shaped and taste of honey, melon, and strawberries. The best time to pick me up for a date is from late spring to early fall. If you pick me up before I am ripe, I'll have a very musky smell.

3. I lay out in the sun and have a wonderful tan. I also despise shaving and have a youthful fuzzy skin. I am green on the inside and have many black seeds

for reproducing. Although I am from New Zealand, make no mistake, I am a fruit, not a bird.

4. I range in size from 1 to 20 pounds. The variety most found visiting the United States are "Solo." My flesh is golden, with an exotic sweet-tart flavor. Inside you will find a collection of gelatin covered seeds.

5. When I went to England, those Brits thought I looked like a pine cone. I am most commonly served as spears, rings or chunks. I grow low to the ground. I get up early every morning to style my killer green hair.

Answers:
1. Star-fruit 2. Guava 3. Kiwi 4. Papaya 5. Pineapple

Epilogue

Some might say that eating raw food is too difficult a challenge. People like the benefits that raw eating provides, but is it really practical? Well, consider the authors of "How We All Went Raw." Both Charles and Stephen live very active collegiate lives and have thrived on an all raw diet for close to three years. They workout hard, study hard, and both are on the honor roll. Another Top Raw Man, George Nungesser, brother of Charles, is an airline pilot who travels around the United States on a weekly basis. He has also traveled to Africa and climbed Mount Kilimanjaro, highest point in Africa, while eating only raw food. The Top Raw Men™ have maintained their active lifestyles on a 100% raw diet.

Letter to the Chef

Dear Master Chef:

I eat only raw foods. Would you be willing to make me a salad that contains only raw vegetables? Please use your creative juices while using the following ingredients as a guide. Remember no cooked or steamed vegetables, only RAW food, please:

Avocado, broccoli, bell peppers (all colors), bok choy, carrots, cauliflower, celery, cilantro, chard, cucumber, Jalapeño pepper (if desired), kale, lettuce (skip the iceberg), mushrooms, onions, parsley, radish, scallions, spinach, sprouts, tomatoes, zucchini.

Thank you for your kind consideration on my behalf.

Sincerely yours,

Your Faithful Customer

The Top Raw Men™ Creed:

We hold these truths to be self evident, that all men are created equal, that they are endowed by their Creator "to eat raw living food."

The Top Raw Men™ in order to obtain better health do solemnly swear to tell the truth, the whole truth, and nothing but the truth—THE MORE BITTER THE MORE BETTER!

When we share the benefits of raw food with our friends, Romans and countrymen, we will be able to speed up that day when all God's children, black men and white men, Jews and Gentiles, Protestants and Catholics will be able to join hands and sing "Raw at last, Raw at last, thank God almighty we are Raw at last!"

The energy, the faith, the devotion which we bring to this endeavor will light our country... and the glow from our 'healthy countenance' can truly light the world.

And so, my fellow Raw Foodist:

Ask not what cooked 'dead' food can do for your body
Ask what your body can do with raw 'living' food

Arranged by George M. Nungesser

APPENDIX

OTHER MATERIALS AVAILABLE

An all raw diet can be prepared without many kitchen appliances. A few sharp knives and a cutting board is all that is required. But some like the ease and convenience that other tools provide. Here are some of our favorite kitchen appliances and materials that we use in preparing our raw meals. Notice that we did not mention the stove, oven, or microwave. Raw Raw Raw!

<u>Dehydrators</u> are great for preparing treats and full meals
    Excalibur® Dehydrators

<u>Juicers</u> make great juice and desserts
    Champion®, Commercial model
    Samson® Juicer
    Green Star® 3000

<u>Blenders</u> are wonderful for smoothies, treats, and desserts for all ages.
    K-Tec® Champ HP3 Blenders

<u>Videos</u> are a relaxing way to improve your knowledge on health related issues.

Call for selection

<u>Books</u> improve your knowledge in health and well being.

Call for selection

<u>Barley Powder Food Supplement</u> is a very important part of the Top Raw Men's™ diet. For information about ordering barley powder food supplements call 1-888-661-7401

All items are subject to availability and prices are subject to change without notice.

Please call for latest price list and information.
888-661-7401.

If you have any suggestions or corrections for our next edition, you may write to The Top Raw Men™.

TOPRAWMEN@CS.COM

Or

WWW.TOPRAWMEN.NET

Endnotes

---

[1] Howell, Edward, M.D., *Enzyme Nutrition*, Avery Publishing Group, Inc., Wayne, NJ, 1985.

[2] Cousens, Gabriel, M.D. M.D.(H), responding to one of Andrew Weil's objections on raw food, article on the internet.

[3] I. Thessalonians 5:21-22, *The Authorized King James Version of 1611*, A. J. Holman Company, Philadelphia.

Recipe Index